F*cks to Give

201 REASONS TO GIVE A SH*T

Remington8
BOOKS

Copyright © 2020 Girl Friday Productions

Remington8
BOOKS

Published by Remington8 Books

Edited and designed by Girl Friday Productions
www.girlfridayproductions.com

Author: L.T. Jenness
Cover and interior design: Rachel Marek
Project management: Alexander Rigby and Leah Jenness

Image credits: All art is from Shutterstock. Cover, 2, 7, lena_nikolaeva; 5, 9, 128, Iliveinoctober; 11, MYMNY; 15, mhatzapa; 17, Anna_leni; 19, Filip1996; 25, Cute Designs Studio; 27, natkacheva; 29, satvarika; 31, Andrew Rybalko; 33, InnaPoka; 35, Zebra Finch; 37, Tanya Syrytsyna; 39, kostolom3000; 43, Slanapotam; 45, monbibi; 47, Maria_Galybina; 53, Taty Vovchek; 55, pashabo; 57, 93, MG Drachal; 61, solmariart; 65, Nicetoseeya; 69, Radiocat; 73, Artnis; 75, judyjump; 77, mcherevan; 79, Bravo Dasha; 81, Olga Milagros; 85, musmellow; 87, sziszigraphics; 91, Amili; 95, EkaterinaP; 97, VectorPlotnikoff; 99, Maaike Boot; 103, Magnia; 107, 123, Olga_Angelloz; 109, Fidan-an; 111, MarushaBelle; 113, Maria Kurty; 115, CPD-Lab; 117, iaodesign; 119, Angelina De Sol; 121, Viktoria Raikina; 125, dottyinkco; 127, nubenamo

ISBN: 978-1-7348802-0-5

First edition

Down to Your Last F*ck?

We've all had those days. Your twenty-minute commute turned into a forty-five-minute slog because a goddamn truck full of goddamn chickens overturned on the interstate. Your cat knocked over your grande latte, spilling it directly onto your laptop, and now your hard drive is fucked. Your rent check got lost in the mail, so you have to talk to your loudmouthed landlord who smells like mothballs and pickles and wears Hawaiian shirts even in winter. And then that hot guy you met last week is ghosting you—WT-ever-loving-F? As if that weren't enough, your own daily dramas are unfolding against this dystopian backdrop: the world is on fire, politics are garbage, and sea turtles are choking on plastic. It's no wonder you feel tired, just so *done*, worn down and out. You've got zero fucks left to give.

We hear you. And we're here to help. With this guided journal, you'll replenish your store of fucks to give. Sure, it may sound cheesy, but gratitude improves your attitude and can fill up your tank when you're running on empty. Really: actual scientists have conducted peer-reviewed studies that found that people who regularly practiced gratitude and wrote about it had better relationships, exercised more, and were healthier and happier than the control groups of grumbling, bitchy crabbypants people.

The prompts in this journal vary. Some will ask you to dig deep, and some will have you focus on what's right in front of your face. In some cases, you'll want to fill pages with writing; in others, a simple list will do. Skip around and fill out the prompts that speak to you in the moment. You'll also find quotes from people a hell of a lot wiser than we are. Let their words inspire you. Finally, you'll also find quick tips, tricks, and suggestions for maximizing your gratitude and refilling your soul.

Once you've filled in your 201 reasons to give a shit, hold on to this journal. You can page through it whenever life ships you fucking cratefuls of lemons; we hope it will help you remember that there are a whole lot of reasons to give a shit, even when life seems bleak.

Now, grab your favorite pen and turn the page. And let's find those fucks to give, one by one.

"When I started counting my blessings, my whole life turned around."

—Willie Nelson

TOTALLY RANDOM . . .
ACTS OF KINDNESS

Every once in a while an ordinary human does something so extraordinarily kind that it renews your faith in what's otherwise the shitshow that is humanity. Write about a time that you were on the receiving end of a random act of kindness. What happened? What was your day or life like before this kindness? How about after? What total rockstar of a homo sapien bestowed it on you?

1. _____

PUTTING IT BACK
OUT THERE

Your turn to step the hell up. Write down three things you can do or have done this week to put a smile on a stranger's face.

2. _____

_____

_____

_____

_____

_____

_____

3. _____

_____

_____

_____

_____

_____

_____

4. _____

_____

_____

_____

_____

_____

_____

"IF YOU GO OUT
AND MAKE SOME
GOOD THINGS
HAPPEN, YOU WILL
FILL THE WORLD
WITH HOPE
AND YOU WILL
FILL YOURSELF
WITH HOPE."

—Barack Obama

THE POWER TO CHANGE YOUR BADITUDE

Sometimes life sucks. But the ability to change your own mind is defi-fucking-nitely something to be grateful for. In the left-hand column below, write about three situations that are bumming you out. In the right-hand column, for each, write a silver lining or some way you can change your outlook.

SHITTY SITUATION	SILVER LINING
5.	
6.	
7.	

"SO OFTEN IN LIFE, THINGS THAT YOU REGARD AS AN IMPEDIMENT TURN OUT TO BE GREAT, GOOD FORTUNE."

—Ruth Bader Ginsburg

THAT ADORABLE AF FURBALL

Look into your pet's eyes and try to tell me you don't give a shit.
(If you can, you're a heartless bitch.) Fill in three things you love
about your cat, dog, hamster, bunny, ferret—hell, even your tortoise,
goldfish, parakeet, or pet snake (you weirdo). And write down one
thing you can do to make him or her happy today.

8. I love . . . _____

_____

_____

_____

_____

_____

9. I love . . . _____

_____

_____

_____

_____

_____

10. I love . . . _____

_____

_____

_____

_____

_____

11. What I'll do to make them happy today: _____

_____

_____

_____

_____

_____

_____

_____

_____

_____

_____

_____

_____

_____

"I think dogs are the most amazing creatures . . . For me they are the role model for being alive."

—Gilda Radner

NO-FUCKING-WAY, HOW-IS-THAT-POSSIBLE COINCIDENCES

What were the chances your favorite sappy love song would come on the jukebox right as your crush walked into the restaurant? How did you bump into your friend from Schenectady in the middle of a crowded street in Morocco? Those no-fucking-way, blow-your-mind coincidences are the magic of this world, friend. Write about a time a coincidence gave you goosebumps.

12. _____

_____

_____

_____

_____

_____

_____

_____

_____

_____

_____

_____

_____

_____

_____

_____

_____

_____

_____

_____

_____

_____

_____

_____

_____

_____

_____

_____

_____

_____

_____

_____

"I DON'T BELIEVE COINCIDENCES
ARE CHANCE EVENTS. I
THINK THEY'RE THE TIMES
WE HAPPEN TO SEE THE
MYSTERIOUS PATTERN WHERE
EVERYTHING IS CONNECTED."

—Julie Gittus

THE INTERNET
(WE KNOW, WE KNOW)

Oh, yeah, most of the time it's the most craptastic bane of modern existence. But sometimes, just sometimes, the internet can plug you in with the rest of humanity, in all its weird, wild, wacky messiness. Write down five sites (a friend's blog? a favorite online magazine? Cat-Bounce.com?) where you can reliably find a glimmer of hope in this wreck of a world.

13. _____

_____

_____

14. _____

_____

_____

15. _____

_____

_____

16. _____

_____

_____

17. _____

_____

_____

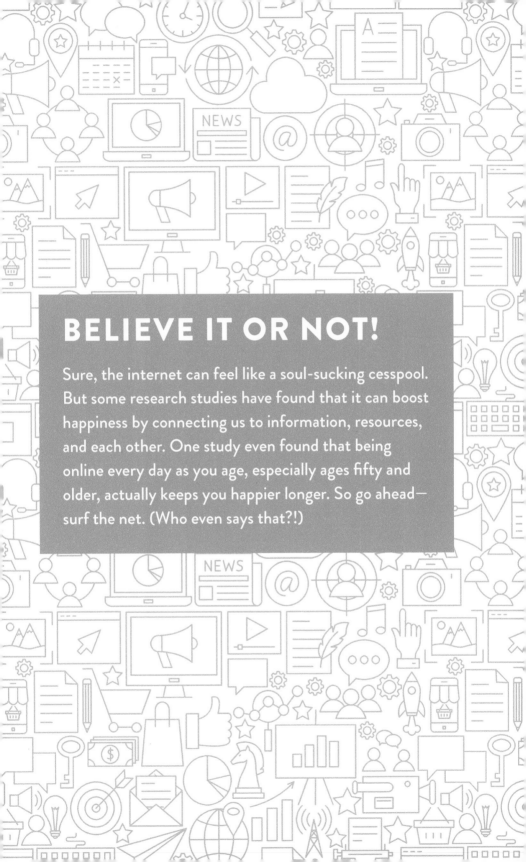

BELIEVE IT OR NOT!

Sure, the internet can feel like a soul-sucking cesspool. But some research studies have found that it can boost happiness by connecting us to information, resources, and each other. One study even found that being online every day as you age, especially ages fifty and older, actually keeps you happier longer. So go ahead—surf the net. (Who even says that?!)

SINGING AT THE TOP OF YOUR LUNGS

Rock. The fuck. Out. Whether you sound like Adele or like hell, sometimes you just have to pull out your internal Janis Joplin and sing it loud. Write down your top three most head-banging, hair-whipping, hands-waving, hell-bent ballads that you perform better than anyone else.

18. SONG	ARTIST

FAVORITE MEMORY ABOUT THIS SONG

19. SONG	ARTIST

FAVORITE MEMORY ABOUT THIS SONG

20.	SONG	ARTIST

FAVORITE MEMORY ABOUT THIS SONG

"THE ONLY THING
BETTER THAN
SINGING IS MORE
SINGING."

—Ella Fitzgerald

FREE FUCKING WILL

No one's the fucking boss of you but Y-O-U. Sure, you need to pay the bills, and there's a certain amount of shit everyone needs to eat to get by in this world. But at the end of the day, the choice is yours and yours alone. And it's a beautiful thing. Write down five things you can choose to do differently this month to feel your power.

21. _____
_____
_____

22. _____
_____
_____

23. _____
_____
_____

24. _____
_____
_____

25. _____
_____
_____
_____

"The best way to not feel hopeless is to get up and do something. Don't wait for good things to happen to you."

—Barack Obama

MEMORABLE MEMES

Thank the goddesses for a good viral kitten video, amiright? Yes, even memes can spark gratitude. Seriously! Describe a meme or two that—admit it—make you chuckle every damn time.

26.

27.

THE MIGHTY MEME

Keyboard cat. The most interesting man in the world. Distracted boyfriend. Drake. Just fucking admit it, they all make you happy. (Full disclosure: "danger noodle" makes us s-n-o-r-t.) And that's OK! According to some psychologists, memes have the power to connect you with your fellow humans, make you feel less alone and more normal, and make you think. All that in a few-bit image with block font. The power!

"ERMAHGERD!"

—Meme

THAT PERSON WHO'S ALWAYS THERE

Who's your ride-or-die bitch? That person in your life you can count on come hell or high water? What do you love most about them? What are the most important moments when you've shown up for each other?

28. My person: _____

_____

What I love about them: _____

_____

_____

_____

_____

_____

_____

_____

_____

_____

_____

_____

_____

_____

_____

_____

_____

_____

_____

_____

Moments when we've shown up: _____

_____

_____

_____

_____

_____

_____

_____

_____

_____

_____

_____

_____

_____

_____

_____

_____

_____

_____

_____

_____

_____

_____

_____

_____

_____

_____

_____

PICTURES TO PROVE IT

Fuck all that noise about digital clutter. Carrying thousands of photos on a device in your pocket keeps you connected to hundreds (tens of thousands?) of moments in your past. What a time to be alive! Open the photo app on your phone and enter a random date into the search bar. What photos pop up? Even if it's just a selfie practicing your duck lips, write what you remember about that moment.

29. _____

"PHOTOGRAPHY HELPS
PEOPLE TO SEE."

—Berenice Abbott

CLAPPING BACK

The world is full of trolls, jerkwads, and basic bitches. But you're a fucking force of nature. Write about one time you clapped back hard at the haters.

30. What happened: _____

_____

_____

_____

_____

_____

_____

_____

_____

_____

_____

_____

_____

_____

_____

_____

_____

_____

_____

_____

_____

_____

_____

How did you feel? _____

_____

_____

_____

_____

_____

_____

_____

_____

_____

_____

_____

_____

_____

_____

_____

_____

_____

_____

_____

_____

_____

_____

_____

_____

_____

OH SNAP!

TAKING A BREAK

Just. Shut. It. Down. Every-damn-thing works better if you unplug it for a minute—including and especially you. You need time to recharge so you can give more fucks! A warm bath by candlelight, a nap in the sun, throwing your phone out the window—what works for you? Write down three ways you plan to give yourself a blissful break this week.

31. _____

_____

_____

_____

_____

_____

32. _____

_____

_____

_____

_____

_____

33. _____

_____

_____

_____

_____

_____

"THERE MUST BE QUITE A FEW THINGS A HOT BATH WON'T CURE, BUT I DON'T KNOW MANY OF THEM."

—Sylvia Plath

THAT DAY YOU SLAYED, ALL DAY

You know what day that was: the day you nailed that presentation, got those digits, felt fine, and turned heads. Oh, honey, you rocked it. Write about a day when you felt on top of the world.

34. _____

_____

_____

_____

_____

_____

_____

_____

_____

_____

_____

_____

_____

_____

_____

_____

_____

_____

_____

_____

_____

_____

_____

_____

_____

_____
_____
_____
_____
_____
_____
_____
_____
_____
_____
_____
_____
_____

YAS
QUEEN
SLAY

GETTING THE FUCK OUT

When your horizon looks bleak as hell at best, a change of scenery can flip that shit right around. Write down five places you could walk or drive to RIGHT NOW to get a new perspective.

35. _____

_____

_____

_____

36. _____

_____

_____

_____

37. _____

_____

_____

_____

38. _____

_____

_____

_____

39. _____

_____

_____

_____

"TO ME A LUSH CARPET OF PINE
NEEDLES OR SPONGY GRASS IS
MORE WELCOME THAN THE MOST
LUXURIOUS PERSIAN RUG."

—Helen Keller

"HOLY SHIT" PLACES

You just can't deny it sometimes. The world is crazy beautiful, man. Describe a place in nature or somewhere outdoors that fills your heart. Include as many sensory details as you can. What does it smell like? What do you hear while you're there? What colors do you see? How does it make you feel?

40. The place: _____

_____

_____

_____

_____

_____

_____

_____

_____

_____

_____

_____

_____

_____

_____

_____

_____

_____

_____

_____

_____

_____

_____

What it's like to be there: _____

_____

_____

_____

_____

_____

_____

_____

_____

_____

_____

_____

_____

_____

_____

_____

_____

_____

_____

_____

_____

_____

_____

_____

_____

_____

_____

FINDING HOME, WHEREVER THE HELL THAT IS

Yeah, yeah, it's cheesy. But it's a cliché for a reason. Home is where the heart is. Where's the place that has your heart?

41. The place: _____

_____

_____

_____

_____

_____

_____

_____

_____

_____

_____

_____

_____

_____

_____

_____

_____

_____

_____

_____

_____

_____

Why it's home: _____

_____

_____

_____

_____

_____

_____

_____

_____

_____

_____

_____

_____

_____

_____

_____

_____

_____

_____

_____

_____

_____

_____

_____

_____

_____

_____

_____

HAPPY PLACES

Sometimes, places are awesome because awesome shit happened there. Where did some good moments of your life unfold? List those places and write one sentence about what happened in each.

42. Happy place:

Happy event:

43. Happy place:

Happy event:

44. Happy place:

Happy event:

45. Happy place:

Happy event:

46. Happy place:

Happy event:

THE SIMPLE SHIT

Sometimes it's the simplest shit, right? Wrapping your hands around a steaming mug of coffee on a rainy day, snuggling under your weighted blanket, sleeping in, scoring an unexpected snow day. Write down ten simple pleasures that are just so plain fucking magical.

47. _____
_____
_____
_____

48. _____
_____
_____
_____

49. _____
_____
_____
_____

50. _____
_____
_____
_____

51. _____
_____
_____

52. _____

_____

_____

_____

_____

53. _____

_____

_____

_____

_____

54. _____

_____

_____

_____

_____

55. _____

_____

_____

_____

_____

56. _____

_____

_____

_____

_____

THE BEST MOMENTS

Dig into those memory banks. There's at least one moment in there when, despite the world being one big fucking dumpster fire, you felt like all was right in your life. Write about it in detail. When was it? Who was there? How did you feel? How do you feel thinking about it now?

57. _____

_____

_____

_____

_____

_____

_____

_____

_____

_____

_____

_____

_____

_____

_____

_____

_____

_____

_____

_____

_____

_____

YOUR FAM

Family is part of the fabric of you. Write about your most fucking fabulous family members—the ones who you share more with than just DNA. Who in your family shows up for you and how?

FAMILY MEMBER	WHY IT'S MORE THAN DNA
58.	
59.	
60.	

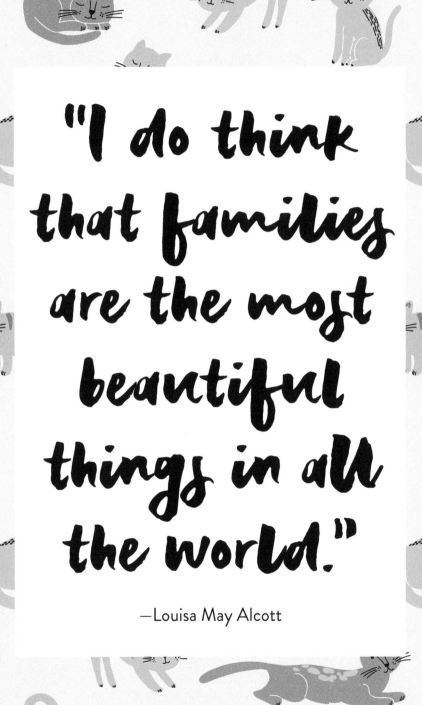

"I do think that families are the most beautiful things in all the world."

—Louisa May Alcott

CHOSEN FAMILY

Who's your brother from another mother? Your sister from another mister? Describe your tribe.

61. Brother from another mother: _____
_____
_____
_____
_____
_____
_____
_____
_____
_____
_____
_____

62. Sister from another mister: _____
_____
_____
_____
_____
_____
_____
_____
_____
_____
_____

63. The rest of the tribe: _____

_____

_____

_____

_____

_____

_____

_____

_____

_____

_____

_____

_____

_____

_____

_____

_____

_____

_____

_____

_____

_____

_____

"IF THE FAMILY YOU CAME FROM
SUCKED, MAKE UP A NEW ONE."

—Lidia Yuknavitch

FRESH AIR

Let's get real: When was the last time you went outside? Not hurrying to your car or running to the store. Like seriously sat, outside, breathing air, and noticing the world around you and being fucking present? Go. Yes, right now. Go outside for fifteen minutes. Breathe, look up and down and around. Then write down what you saw and how it made you feel.

64.

_____

_____

_____

_____

_____

_____

_____

_____

_____

_____

_____

_____

_____

_____

_____

_____

"Some old-fashioned things like fresh air and sunshine are hard to beat."

—Laura Ingalls Wilder

TALKING THE TALK

There are the people you party with, the people you plan big things with, the people you work out with . . . and then there are the easy-as-fucking-pie relationships where all you need is that person, a cup of coffee, and hours to just talk and be. Who is your person? What's it like to be with them?

65. _____

_____
_____
_____
_____
_____
_____
_____
_____
_____
_____
_____
_____
_____
_____
_____
_____
_____
_____
_____
_____
_____

"YOU, ME, AND FIVE BUCKS."

—*Reality Bites*

YOUR GO-TO FOLKS

And then there are those people you can lean on when shit goes sideways. If it's 2:00 a.m. and you're locked out of your home, if you're in Cozumel and your wallet and passport got stolen, if you pop a tire on the interstate—these are the people you can rely on. Who's on your speed dial when the crapola hits the air-conditioning? Describe a time each one showed up for you.

66. _____

_____

_____

_____

_____

_____

_____

_____

_____

_____

_____

_____

_____

_____

_____

_____

_____

_____

_____

67. _____

_____

_____

_____

_____

_____

_____

_____

_____

_____

_____

_____

_____

_____

_____

68. _____

_____

_____

_____

_____

_____

_____

_____

_____

_____

_____

_____

_____

_____

FOCUSING ON OTHER PEOPLE

Sometimes, giving more—and more of yourself—to others is the best way to feel gratitude. Weird, right? But you know that shit's real. Write about a time when helping out a fellow human made you feel good. Write down something you can do in the near future to make someone else's day.

69. I felt good when I helped . . . _____

_____

_____

_____

_____

_____

_____

_____

70. Here's something I can do soon: _____

_____

_____

_____

_____

_____

_____

_____

_____

_____

"Always do the right thing."

—Da Mayor

BEING A WASTE OF SPACE

Yeah, YOLO, carpe diem, and all that motivational shit is great. But you know what feels fucking amazing sometimes? Just letting it all go and chilling the hell out. Be a waste of space, a lump on the couch— hell, don't even get out of bed. Just watch crap on YouTube on your phone. Describe your ideal do-nothing day.

71. _____

"IT IS NICE TO THINK HOW ONE CAN
BE RECKLESSLY LOST IN A DAISY!"

—Anne Morrow Lindbergh

FRIEND DATES!

The best pick-me-up in the whole world is a date with one of your besties. In the space below, write down the names of your closest friends and one fucking fantastic friend date you can go on.

72. Person: _____

Ideal friend date: _____

_____

_____

_____

_____

_____

73. Person: _____

Ideal friend date: _____

_____

_____

_____

_____

_____

74. Person: _____

Ideal friend date: _____

_____

_____

_____

_____

_____

_____

_____

"Walk away from 'friendships' that make you feel small and insecure, and seek out people who inspire you and support you."

—Michelle Obama

ESCAPING WITH A GOOD BOOK

Reading connects us with ourselves and the world. We're talking about reading books, not top 10 listicles online or the latest breaking news that everything is going to hell in a handbasket. List your top three favorite books, and why you love them.

75. Title: _____

_____

Why you love it: _____

_____

_____

_____

_____

_____

_____

76. Title: _____

_____

Why you love it: _____

_____

_____

_____

_____

_____

_____

77. Title: _____

_____

Why you love it: _____

_____

_____

_____

_____

_____

_____

_____

_____

_____

_____

_____

_____

_____

_____

_____

_____

_____

_____

"I HAVE A STRONG OPINION THAT
A GENUINE LOVE OF BOOKS IS
ONE OF THE GREATEST BLESSINGS
OF LIFE FOR MAN AND WOMAN."

—Sara Coleridge

SUN SALUTATION, MOTHERFUCKER

Stating the fucking obvious here: You have a body. When's the last time you really appreciated it? Take fifteen minutes now and s-t-r-e-t-c-h. Stand with your arms at your sides. Inhale and sweep your arms up in a wide arc, stretching at the top. Exhale and sweep your arms down to your sides, folding at the waist. Repeat. Shit—carefully, now, you're no Simone Biles. The point is to move your body and appreciate every muscle. Write about what you felt doing this exercise, and write down a few ways you can incorporate some conscious movement every day.

78. How I felt: _____

_____

_____

_____

_____

79. Daily movement: _____

_____

_____

_____

_____

_____

_____

_____

_____

"I AM PERSUADED THAT THE GREATER PART OF OUR COMPLAINTS ARISE FROM WANT OF EXERCISE."

—Madame de Sévigné

TAKING TIME TO SMELL THE FUCKING ROSES

Have you ever noticed that a good smell can transport you? A whiff of someone's perfume can snap you right back to a first date. The aroma of something baking in the oven can remind you of childhood. What are some simple scents that give you all the feels?

80. Scent: _____

Where does it take you?: _____

_____

_____

_____

_____

81. Scent: _____

Where does it take you?: _____

_____

_____

_____

_____

82. Scent: _____

Where does it take you?: _____

_____

_____

_____

_____

83. Scent: _____
Where does it take you?: _____
_____
_____
_____
_____
_____
_____

84. Scent: _____
Where does it take you?: _____
_____
_____
_____
_____
_____
_____
_____
_____
_____
_____
_____
_____

"SMELL THE ROSES. SMELL
THE COFFEE. WHATEVER IT IS
THAT MAKES YOU HAPPY."

—Rita Moreno

GROOVING

You just can't help it. When certain tunes come on, no matter how crappy your mood, your toes can't be stopped from tapping, your head can't help but bob. What songs have the power to flip your frown upside-down?

85. Song: _____

Band: _____

Memory of the song: _____

_____

86. Song: _____

Band: _____

Memory of the song: _____

_____

87. Song: _____

Band: _____

Memory of the song: _____

_____

88. Song: _____

Band: _____

Memory of the song: _____

_____

89. Song: _____

Band: _____

Memory of the song: _____

_____

"WITHOUT MUSIC, LIFE WOULD BE A MISTAKE."

—Friedrich Nietzsche

SCREEN TIME AND CHILLING

Isn't a weekend binge-watch just heavenly? Getting lost in a world created in a movie or TV show is escapism at its best. What are some shows or movies that you find oh-so damn delightful?

90. Movie: _____

Why do you love it? _____

_____

_____

91. Movie: _____

Why do you love it? _____

_____

_____

92. Movie: _____

Why do you love it? _____

_____

_____

_____

93. Movie: _____

Why do you love it? _____

_____

_____

_____

94. Movie: _____

Why do you love it? _____

_____

_____

95. Show: _____

Why do you love it? _____

_____

96. Show: _____

Why do you love it? _____

_____

97. Show: _____

Why do you love it? _____

_____

98. Show: _____

Why do you love it? _____

_____

99. Show: _____

Why do you love it? _____

_____

"Everything I
learned I learned
from the movies."

—Audrey Hepburn

TGI-MOTHERFUCKING-F!

Happy Friday, bitches! Oh, how we live for the weekend. Weekends are YOUR time to do as much or as little as you want to do. All right, you weekend warrior, you: Write a description of your perfect weekend. Do you sleep in? Get up early while the world is still quiet? Are there pancakes involved?! Do you stay put or do you head for the hills? Dish the deets here.

100. _____

_____

_____

_____

_____

_____

_____

_____

_____

_____

_____

_____

_____

_____

_____

_____

_____

_____

_____

_____

_____

ROCK YOUR WEEKEND

Have Saturday and Sunday been a little lackluster lately? Here are ideas from mental health experts and happiness gurus for maximizing your time.

- Get moving. That's right: exercise! (Don't roll your eyes at me.) Take a long hike, walk around a mall for fuck's sake—just move.
- Hang out. Make your weekends about your people. Set up plans with friends and fam.
- Handle your shit. It's OK to do a little bit of work on the weekend to set yourself up for success.
- Say OHM, m-fer. Try meditating or do something else to allow yourself to just chill for a minute.

COMFORT FOOD

OMFG, after the shittiest day, diving into a heaping plate of mac 'n' cheese never felt so good. Bad breakup? We have a meatball recipe for that. Laid off? Hello, cookie dough. There is nothing wrong with eating your feelings, and if anyone says otherwise, tell them to fuck all the way off. Describe the five meals that give you life when life kicks you in the ass.

101. _____

_____

_____

_____

_____

_____

_____

_____

_____

102. _____

_____

_____

_____

_____

_____

_____

_____

_____

103. _____

_____

_____

_____

_____

_____

_____

_____

_____

104. _____

_____

_____

_____

_____

_____

_____

_____

_____

_____

105. _____

_____

_____

_____

_____

_____

_____

_____

_____

EATING REAL SHIT

On the other hand, sometimes it feels best to do your body good. Yes, we're talking eating healthy shit: fruits, veggies, whole grains. Write down an easy, healthy weekday lunch that you can commit to making for yourself this week to feel good.

106. _____

_____

_____

_____

_____

_____

_____

_____

_____

_____

_____

_____

_____

_____

_____

_____

_____

_____

_____

_____

NO EXCUSES

Think it's too hard to be healthy? Suck it up. Here are super-easy snacks that are good for you too.

- Spice that shit up: Sprinkle sliced veggies with lime and flavored salt, chile powder, or a Middle Eastern spice mix.
- Peanut butter and apples, celery, or crackers— whatever makes you feel like your mom just made you an afterschool snack. There's a reason it's the ultimate comfort food.
- Get a fine cheese—we mean the expensive stuff— and put a thick slab on a cracker. Heaven.
- Cut up a bunch of fruit, then slide it onto a skewer, if you're feeling a Martha Stewart vibe.
- Savor the hell out of some delicious chocolate—just make it dark with plenty of cacao.

TREATING YO'SELF

Hey, queen. You deserve a massage, a fancy dinner, that fine vegan leather jacket you've been eyeing. Yes, you do. You are fucking worth it. Write down five ways you plan to pamper yourself next time you're feeling out of gas.

107. _____
_____
_____
_____

108. _____
_____
_____
_____

109. _____
_____
_____
_____

110. _____
_____
_____
_____

111. _____
_____
_____

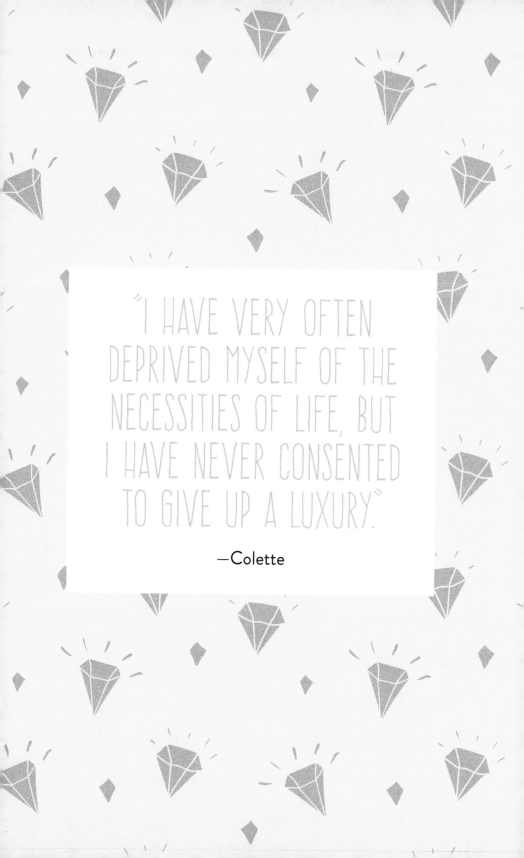

"I HAVE VERY OFTEN
DEPRIVED MYSELF OF THE
NECESSITIES OF LIFE, BUT
I HAVE NEVER CONSENTED
TO GIVE UP A LUXURY."

—Colette

GETTING YOUR SHIT TOGETHER

Don't worry. We're not going to go all Marie Kondo on you. But making sense of that pile of papers, that junk drawer, that corner of your room collecting dirty socks—it can give you the zip you need. Take fifteen minutes now and put some rule over something unruly. How did it make you feel?

112. _____

_____

_____

_____

_____

_____

_____

_____

_____

_____

_____

_____

"I MAKE NO SECRET OF THE FACT THAT I WOULD RATHER LIE ON A SOFA THAN SWEEP BENEATH IT."

—Shirley Conran

NEED SOME CLEANSPIRATION?

There are p-l-e-n-t-y of tasks that you can do in fifteen minutes or less. Here are three you can try *today*.

- Pick a room and wipe down those dusty-ass blinds.
- Actually put that laundry away after you fold it instead of setting it on a chair by your dresser for two more days.
- Set your timer and and purge as much stuff as you can from a closet or dresser.

GIGGLE FITS

Yes, even as grown-ass women, there have been times that we have nearly pissed ourselves laughing. And you know what? We felt A-L-I-V-E. Write about a time you almost literally cried from laughing. Who was there? What happened? Are you laughing just thinking about it?

113. _____

_____

_____

_____

_____

_____

_____

_____

_____

_____

_____

_____

_____

_____

_____

_____

_____

_____

_____

_____

_____

_____

_____

"LIFE IS SO
TOUGH . . . YOU
BETTER LAUGH
AT EVERYTHING."

—Joan Rivers

GETTING LUCKY

No, not that way. Get your mind out of the goddamn gutter, man. We're talking about the four-leaf-clover kind. Have you ever had a stroke of luck that's left you wide-eyed and slack-jawed and saying, "I am one lucky bastard"? Write about it here.

114. _____

CHOCOLATE . . . JUST CHOCOLATE

We live in a world that has chocolate. I mean, do you need more than that to feel lucky to be alive? (The answer is no, you ungrateful human.) Really, though, sweet treats are sometimes all you need to make your day damn delicious. What are your guilty pleasure desserts?

115. _____

_____

_____

116. _____

_____

_____

117. _____

_____

_____

118. _____

_____

_____

119. _____

_____

_____

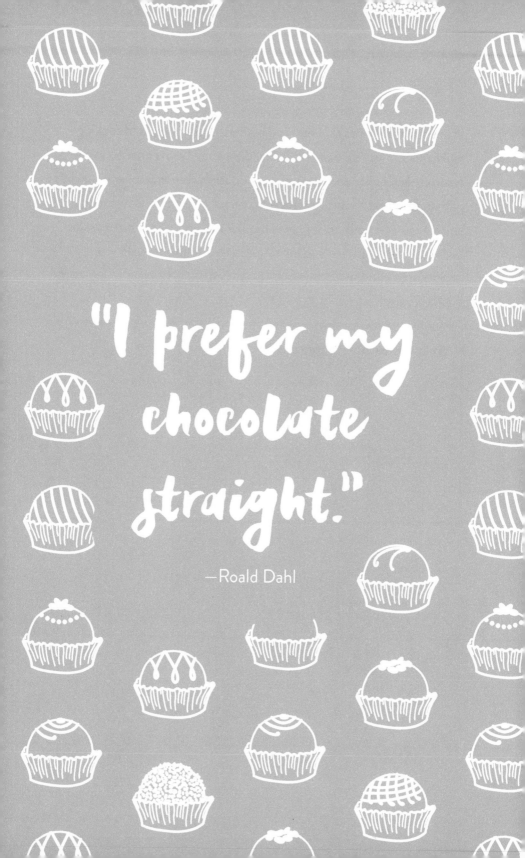

"I prefer my chocolate straight."

—Roald Dahl

BIG PLANS

What special events do you have bolded, underlined, and fucking *highlighted* in your calendar? It could be a fancy-ass charity event where there's glitz and glamor. Your cousin's wedding, where you'll get smashed with your fun uncle. Even your work holiday party, where you and your colleague will spike the nog. What out-of-the-ordinary occasions are you looking forward to in the near future?

120. Event:

What you're looking forward to:

121. Event:

What you're looking forward to:

122. Event:

What you're looking forward to:

123. Event:

What you're looking forward to:

DRESSING TO IMPRESS

We know you can turn heads in your goddamn sweats. But you also clean up real nice, and sometimes dressing fine can have you feeling fine. Describe your version of a power suit: that ensemble that makes you feel like the queen you really are.

124. _____

_____

_____

_____

_____

_____

_____

_____

_____

_____

_____

_____

_____

_____

_____

_____

"YOU CAN HAVE ANYTHING YOU WANT IN LIFE IF YOU DRESS FOR IT."

—Edith Head

PUT ON YOUR THINKING CLOTHES

Your threads can communicate who you are to the world, sure. And you know getting all dolled up makes you feel fine. But studies show that looking fly can also affect how you think. That's right: Dressing fancy can increase your abstract thinking as well as open up your perspective. All the more reason for a shopping spree.

FEELING GOOD AS HELL

Look in the mirror. Hey there, hot stuff. Feeling yourself? You fucking bet. Write down ten things you love about you. Don't skimp on the details!

125. _____

_____

_____

_____

_____

126. _____

_____

_____

_____

_____

127. _____

_____

_____

_____

_____

128. _____

_____

_____

_____

_____

129. _____

_____

_____

_____

130. _____
_____
_____
_____

131. _____
_____
_____
_____

132. _____
_____
_____
_____

133. _____
_____
_____
_____

134. _____
_____
_____
_____

OLD FRIENDS

You've known them since you ate Play-Doh. They were there when you made a goddamn fool of yourself in front of Hot Guy from Bio Class in middle school. They were friends with you even when you had braces and those shitty, shitty bangs. Who are the old friends you can be stupid with?

135. Person:

Friends since . . .

136. Person:

Friends since . . .

137. Person:

Friends since . . .

"Many people will walk in and out of your life, but only true friends will leave footprints in your heart."

—Eleanor Roosevelt

NEW FRIENDS

List some cool people in your life who are new friends or who have that friend-potential vibe. Right now, commit to a plan to invite them to hang out. Write that shit down so you won't forget. What will you do?

138. Person:

Hangout:

139. Person:

Hangout:

140. Person:

Hangout:

"IN MEETING
AGAIN AFTER
A SEPARATION,
ACQUAINTANCES
ASK AFTER OUR
OUTWARD LIFE,
FRIENDS AFTER
OUR INNER LIFE."

—Marie von Ebner-Eschenbach

THE PEOPLE IN YOUR NEIGHBORHOOD

Sometimes, that fucking brilliant banter you have with the checkout lady at the grocery store just makes your day. Or it's that crossing guard who always says good morning when you're stopped at his light. Describe the people you don't know well but see regularly who put a smile on your face just by being them.

141. _____

_____

_____

_____

142. _____

_____

_____

_____

143. _____

_____

_____

_____

144. _____

_____

_____

_____

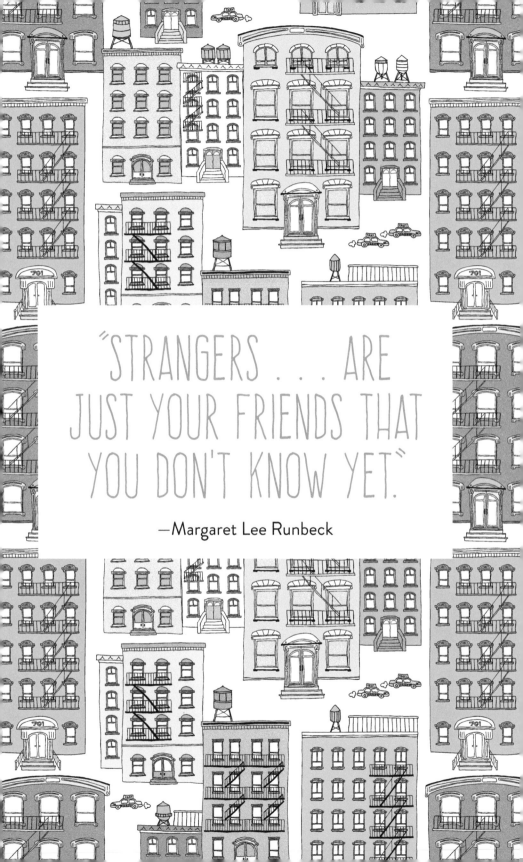

"STRANGERS . . . ARE JUST YOUR FRIENDS THAT YOU DON'T KNOW YET."

—Margaret Lee Runbeck

DATES WITH YOURSELF

In the frenzy of the everyday, it can be hard to slow down and connect with YOU. You need alone time every now and again to do shit that makes you feel like you. Write down five perfect dates you can take yourself on so you can clear your head and make all the other crap melt away.

145. _____

_____

_____

_____

_____

146. _____

_____

_____

_____

_____

147. _____

_____

_____

_____

_____

_____

148. _____

149. _____

"I PAINT SELF-PORTRAITS BECAUSE I
AM SO OFTEN ALONE, BECAUSE
I AM THE SUBJECT I KNOW BEST."

—Frida Kahlo

RAIN AND SHINE

Every type of weather brings with it some sort of comfort, whether it's that first early-summer night when you don't need a hoodie, the perfect gray day to curl up with a cat and book, or your first snow day of the year. You're smiling right now thinking about it, we know. It's some good shit. Describe what you look forward to in . . .

150. Spring: _____

_____

_____

_____

151. Summer: _____

_____

_____

_____

152. Fall: _____

_____

_____

_____

153. Winter: _____

_____

_____

_____

_____

"If we had no winter,
the spring would
not be so pleasant."

—Anne Bradstreet

YOUR STUFF

Professional organizers on *Hoarders* be damned. Keepsakes, heirlooms, stuff can give you comfort and can make home feel like home. What are your most prized possessions? Why do you love them so much?

154. Prized possession:

What does it make you feel?

155. Prized possession:

What does it make you feel?

156. Prized possession:

What does it make you feel?

157. Prized possession:

What does it make you feel?

158. Prized possession:

What does it make you feel?

MEMORY LANE

It's time to go back. Way the hell back. Break out that middle school yearbook, high school scrapbook, or baby book your mom gave you. Don't cringe! Flip through the pages. What happy memories does it spark? What valuable life lessons did you learn during that time?

159. Memory: _____

_____

_____

_____

_____

_____

_____

_____

_____

160. Memory: _____

_____

_____

_____

_____

_____

_____

_____

_____

_____

161. Life lesson: _____

_____
_____
_____
_____
_____
_____
_____
_____
_____
_____
_____
_____

162. Life lesson: _____

_____
_____
_____
_____
_____
_____
_____
_____
_____
_____
_____

SAYING THANK YOU

In this age of texting instead of calling, emailing instead of dragging your ass to the post office to mail a letter, and simply posting "Thanks, all!" on Facebook, it's probably been years, nay, friggin' eons since you've written a proper thank-you note to . . . anyone. Draft one here, and write how you feel when you're done.

163. Dear _____ , _____

_____

_____

_____

_____

_____

_____

_____

_____

_____

_____

_____

_____

_____

_____

_____

_____

_____

_____

_____

_____

_____

_____

164. How do you feel now? _____

_____

_____

_____

_____

_____

_____

_____

_____

_____

_____

_____

_____

_____

_____

_____

_____

_____

_____

_____

_____

_____

_____

THE DETAILS

It's time to zoom in. Like way, way the hell in. Think about the tiniest details in life that bring you joy—the things that you could focus on with a macro lens and snap a photo of. Maybe it's a baby's pinky toe (heart-eyes emoji!). Maybe it's a tiny blossom starting to unfurl on a primrose tree. Maybe it's the light reflecting off a butterfly's wing. List the details that matter to you here.

165. _____

166. _____

167. _____

168. _____

169. _____

170. _____

171. _____

172. _____

173. _____

174. _____

"THOSE WHO WISH TO KNOW ABOUT THE WORLD MUST LEARN ABOUT IT IN ITS PARTICULAR DETAILS."

—Heracleitus

GETTING WISE

You can look at getting older as life just going downhill, one more shitty step toward the grave. Or you can look at getting older as getting wiser. (Stop rolling your eyes!) Write down some wisdom you've earned along the way.

175. _____

"There is a wisdom of the head, and a wisdom of the heart."

—Charles Dickens

LIVING TO TELL THE TALE

Made it by the skin of your teeth? Dodged a damn bullet? Gave a
huge fucking sigh of relief? Write about a high-pressure moment
you made it through.

176. _____

_____

_____

_____

_____

_____

_____

_____

_____

_____

_____

_____

_____

_____

_____

_____

_____

_____

_____

_____

_____

_____

_____

_____

MODERN MARVELS

It's easy to take all the conveniences of our modern world for granted. But flying in a plane? Having thousands of movies streaming at your fingertips? Using an electric toothbrush? Turning on the air-conditioning to comfortably survive global warming? It's all fucking amazing when you stop to think about it. Don't take it for granted. What modern luxuries are you grateful for?

177. _____

_____

_____

178. _____

_____

_____

179. _____

_____

_____

180. _____

_____

_____

181. _____

_____

_____

182. _____
_____
_____
_____
_____

183. _____
_____
_____
_____
_____

184. _____
_____
_____
_____
_____

185. _____
_____
_____
_____
_____

186. _____
_____
_____
_____
_____

YOUR AMAZING PERSONALITY

There's only one you. What do you love about your inner self? What are your most bitchin' qualities? What parts of your persona leave you fucking dazzled? Write about them, free form, here.

187. _____

_____
_____
_____
_____
_____
_____
_____
_____
_____
_____
_____
_____
_____
_____
_____
_____
_____
_____
_____
_____
_____
_____

GETTING SHIT DONE

It feels so damn good to check stuff off a to-do list, doesn't it? Taking care of business can also give you the momentum to tackle bigger projects and frees up brain space to devote to fun stuff. Write down five things you accomplished today. They could be as simple as making your bed to delivering that big report to your boss.

188. _____
_____
_____
_____

189. _____
_____
_____
_____

190. _____
_____
_____
_____

191. _____
_____
_____
_____

192. _____
_____
_____
_____

CHECK OFF THOSE GODDAMN TO-DOS

Are you a slacker struggling to reform? A procrastinator praying for motivation? Try shaking things up. Here are some ideas:

- Get up earlier. Seeing the sunrise can give you the oomph you need to start the day right.
- Simplify. Do you have forty-two things on your to-do list before 10:00 a.m.? That's just not possible. Give yourself a break and figure out what's truly manageable in the time you have. Sometimes, that means setting boundaries and saying no.
- Do the worst / hardest / least-enjoyable thing RIGHT NOW. Start your day with the worst thing you have to do. It can only get better from there.
- Go to sleep. How can you be productive if your brain is a sleep-deprived slug? How can you produce straight fire when you're burnt out? Sometimes you just need to reset and refuel.

UNCRAPPY COWORKERS

We've all got horror stories about coworkers. That person who marks every damn email as urgent. Your cubiclemate who chews kettle chips so loudly it makes you want to slam your head against your desk . . . But working with people you actually like, people who help make the hours between nine and five pass without pissing you off? Now that's something to thank your lucky stars for. Write down the names of three coworkers and what you like about them.

193. _____

_____

_____

_____

_____

_____

_____

_____

_____

_____

_____

_____

_____

_____

_____

_____

_____

_____

194. _____

_____

_____

_____

_____

_____

_____

_____

195. _____

_____

_____

_____

_____

_____

_____

_____

_____

_____

_____

_____

_____

_____

_____

FAIL!

We know you so don't want to, but think back to a time you fucked up: you and only you botched that presentation, totally tanked in the volleyball finals, had a miscalculation of disastrous proportions. This might seem counterintuitive, but finding gratitude even in your failures makes you a fucking Jedi Master of mind over matters-at-hand. Describe in detail two of your most epic fails, and see if you can find something in them to be grateful for.

196.

197.

TODAY

Sometimes, when you have zero fucks to give, you gotta dig deep and find those fucks. It can be work, but getting in the habit of doing it will help you tons. Think about your day—even if it was a shitty, shitty day—and search for three things that made it meaningful. We bet if you can find three fucks to give, you'll find a few extras.

198. _____

_____

_____

_____

199. _____

_____

_____

_____

200. _____

_____

_____

_____

201. Extras: _____

_____

_____

_____

_____

_____

Thank F*cking Goodness!

You did it. You journaled your way to not one, not two, but 201 reasons to give a shit. We hope in the process you've managed to refill your heart and the fucks you have to give. Existence is rough, friend, and the world (and people and circumstances outside of your control) will continue to try you. You can meet it with an open heart and damn grateful soul. And when needed, return to the work you did in this journal. We know you'll find you've got oh-so-many fucks left to give.

"WEAR GRATITUDE
LIKE A CLOAK,
AND IT WILL FEED
EVERY CORNER
OF YOUR LIFE."

—Rūmī